Living

FULL CIRCLE

Andrea,
Sharing your gifts
with the world
is making a
difference.
Keep showing up
as your authentic
Self. xo
Jenene.

52 Week Undated Planner
for Living with Balance and Intention
Inspired by Medicine Wheel Teachings

Jenene Wooldridge

ACORNPRESS

Foreword by Elder Noel Milliea

I want to take this time to congratulate Jenene on her amazing work on this project, which is probably not a project but a passion. The essence of Balance as it relates to all four quadrants of the medicine wheel is about knowing where you personally are at this very moment in each one of these four quadrants (physical, mental, emotional and spiritual). Through a sincere desire for change we begin this journey inward and we embrace the simplicity rather than the complications of life on life's terms.

Through this process we have come to realize that gratitude is the cornerstone to change. After working for many years within the justice system, I always remember a statement that a Native offender who was serving a life sentence told me: "Nothing Changes if Nothing Changes." This is a very powerful statement and as I was developing this healing model of the medicine wheel, I reflected on this notion of change.

The search for Balance through self-discovery of our hidden or unseen potential can be one of the most amazing and beautiful journeys we can embark on. Always keep in mind that it is not so much about achieving balance but more so the journey or the search for balance that is the key to healing our wounded spirits.

So again, thanks Jenene for the honor of allowing me to be a part of this amazing journey.

Nogemagh/All My Relations
Elder Noel Milliea

About Me

I am the daughter of former Chief James (Jim) and Carolyn Sark. I come from a long line of leaders including hereditary and elected Chiefs. My father was raised in Lennox Island with his parents, my 'Grammy Mitchell' (the late Alma Cormier Sark Mitchell) and his father Chief Jacob Sark. His grandfather, and my great grandfather, former Chief John Thomas Sark who was also hereditary Mi'kmaq Chief, and from the Peju clan on Epekwitk (Prince Edward Island). His wife was Margaret Thornton. She too was Mi'kmaw but adopted by an Irish family.

My mother also grew up in Lennox Island with her parents, my late 'Grandfather' John Andrew and 'Grammy Francis' Emma (Gallant) Francis. John Andrew was the son of the late Mary Alice (Barlow) Francis (also adopted) from Indian Island, and John P. Francis from Lennox Island. Emma's parents were Peter Andrew Gallant and Mary Isabelle Gauthier from Rustico.

I grew up in Kuntal Kwesawe'kl (Rocky Point). Epekwitk is my ancestral home, the territory of the Mi'kmaq, and part of Mi'kma'ki. As Mi'kmaq, we are descendants of our ancestors. In our culture, younger people generally look to Elders who are humble, respected, and knowledgeable. Many respected Elders have gone through a healing journey of their own. Elders may provide advice, wisdom, and comfort to younger generations. They usually have great connection to culture and community, hold traditional teachings and values, as well as knowledge about our past and our ancestors.

I have a responsibility to nurture and protect Mother Earth, as well as leave the world better than I found it. Part of this includes helping others with their journey. I have gifts to share that I learned through my own healing journey. Through this planner, I offer you key learnings from the time I have spent committed to my own growth mindset journey. Take what you need and use it as best helps you. I am guided by my ancestors, my Elders and spiritual teachers.

A number of years ago, I committed to improving a little bit each day. I realized no matter what life throws our way, we still have an opportunity to improve our own well-being and happiness. It starts with us. Changing your thoughts, digging deep, and aligning your heart and mind ultimately changes your world.

Before this work, as a professional woman, wife and mother of two, I was pulled in many directions. There weren't enough hours in the day to do everything I wanted. I had a constant feeling I was missing something in my life. When I was unbalanced I felt tired, overwhelmed and anxious at times.

In a search for growth and balance I started reading books and listening to podcasts based on personal development and having a growth mindset. It wasn't until I was able to ground myself in nature and get back to my spirit that I was able to break through my fears and self-doubt. I realized they were holding me back from living authentically and fully. It became clear I had one shot at life and I wasn't going to let it go by without giving it my all.

I started living with intention and decided to harness my focus on healing, building resiliency, prioritizing the importance of planning and creating balance that worked for me. Having balance in life doesn't mean ensuring that there are equal parts in all areas of life, it means prioritizing what is important and living life in alignment with what is important to you. I became very intentional on how I spent my time and ensured that it was improving my life.

Imagine life as a game in which you are juggling five balls in the air. You name them – work, family, health, friends and spirit – and you're keeping all of these in the air. You will soon understand that work is a rubber ball; if you drop it, it will bounce back.

But the other four balls – family, health, friends and spirit – are made of glass. If you drop one of these, they will be irrevocably scuffed, marked, nicked, damaged, or even shattered. They will never be the same. - Brian Dyson

You may find yourself pulled in various directions and juggling many balls. It is in times like these that you must set and maintain boundaries with what is important to you. Sometimes I will drop balls but living with balance assures I don't drop my glass balls.

Over 10 years ago, a friend gifted a quote to me, and I placed it on the mirror in my bedroom. It became a visual cue for me each day. I have read the same Esther Hicks quote every morning since then:

"You are the vibrational writers of the script of your life, and everyone else in the Universe is playing the part that you have assigned to them."

The way we speak, the way we act and the choices we make influence our journey in life.

The path for our intentional lifestyle will look different for each of us. Before we start down that path it is important to determine what exactly it is we want for our life, how we are feeling in all areas of our life, and take the time to identify what we need and how we will create it. A gentle reminder, forward is forward no matter your pace.

Incorporating boosters including journaling, gratitude, affirmations, exercise, volunteering, joy and meditation will create your best life. When I commit to something, it's usually all or nothing. Over six months, I incorporated drastic changes to my routine and habits. While this list can look daunting, it did not happen overnight. This is the importance of incorporating small daily habits. It may not seem like a huge change, but it can add up to a lot over time.

In 2019 I decided to make drastic changes to my daily routine (nothing like a good jolt to the body!) including:

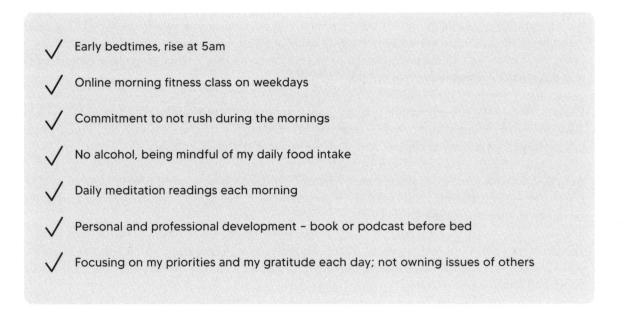

✓ Early bedtimes, rise at 5am

✓ Online morning fitness class on weekdays

✓ Commitment to not rush during the mornings

✓ No alcohol, being mindful of my daily food intake

✓ Daily meditation readings each morning

✓ Personal and professional development – book or podcast before bed

✓ Focusing on my priorities and my gratitude each day; not owning issues of others

Implementing these habits changed my life. I made big and small changes along the way and incorporated routines that work for me. I focused so much more attention on what my spirit needed. What works for me in creating my best lifestyle and living with intention may not work for you. You will know what suits your life and soul best.

Introduction

After becoming a mother of two I realized that planning is not just important but necessary to make life manageable. I wanted a planner where I could write it all down in, one that could handle my plans, my personal and professional notes. I started by setting aside thirty minutes every Sunday to create a blueprint of my week ahead.

Planning and setting intentions and goals help us to identify our focus. This sets the tone for how you are going to invest your time and energy. In taking time to reflect and celebrate successes we are able to track what works and what doesn't. This planner will assist you in setting your tone for the year and walk you through the weeks and months ahead.

Each month focuses on key lessons and reflections I have learned to support you on your journey. While all of these small changes are beneficial in the immediate future, the real value is the growth you will see over the years. By implementing balance and intentional living, you will see big successes. Using the medicine wheel framework will assist you on your journey and help to achieve awareness in your life around your physical, mental, emotional and spiritual status. Being able to reflect on these areas and how they are interconnected will allow you to identify what you may need to incorporate in these areas for you to be the best version of yourself. As you do this work, your life will come into alignment with your desired path. You will feel more at peace with yourself than ever before. As you move into this journey, you will reflect on where you need to reset, where you are going to spend your energy, what brings your soul joy, how you want to feel, and what steps you need to take to make it happen!

Medicine Wheel Teachings
Balance Intention and Interconnectedness

Medicine Wheel Teachings - Balance, Intention and Interconnectedness

There are many Indigenous teachings around the medicine wheel. In this planner, you use the medicine wheel as a tool for living life with balance and intention. Being aware of where you are physically, mentally, emotionally and spiritually allows you to identify areas that may need more work in your life. It allows you to improve on those and ultimately live in greater harmony. In order for you to make the external world a better place you must start with yourself and look internally.

The medicine wheel is an important symbol within Indigenous teachings and other aspects of culture and life, although it is important to note that not all Indigenous groups use medicine wheel teachings nor do they call it that. For the purpose of this planner, it is used as a framework to represent the importance of balance, interconnectedness and harmony in life. Alignment with this framework can generate energy to create personal empowerment.

Over the years, teachings of the medicine wheel have been shared with me and I acknowledge there are many teachings and variations. I have been able to incorporate those teachings as a self-assessment tool around balancing the quadrants in my life planning. The self-assessment and reflection allow me to determine what is working, what is not and where greater attention is needed in the various aspects of my life. I am dedicated to personal and professional development and I am sharing the teachings that speak to me and work in my life.

The circle of the medicine wheel is divided into four quadrants – physical, mental, emotional and spiritual. It can also represent the four seasons, four directions and four sacred medicines. In order to create balance and improve one's overall being, you must identify the needs of each interconnected state of being. The circle of the medicine wheel represents the circle of life and the balance needed in those areas of life.

Being aware of where you are with regards to your physical, mental, emotional and spiritual state is the first step in moving towards balance in your life. It is important to take time to reflect on those areas of your life. What areas are being fulfilled? What areas are lacking?

As Indigenous people, we have been planning ahead for millennia. This planning included looking ahead for seven generations to ensure that resources were available for future generations. We lived and made choices in a self-determined way, which is as important today as it was then. To live your best life, you are to live with intention and think about how it will impact future generations. It is about living mindfully and with good intention.

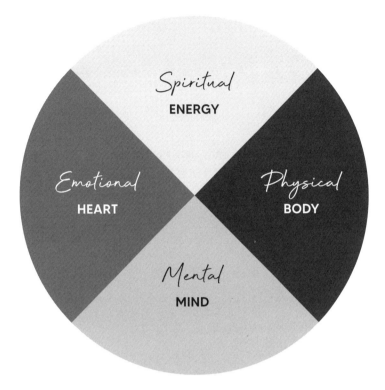

Planning ahead and living in a good way are incorporated through other Indigenous teachings including the seven sacred teachings – Wisdom, Love, Respect, Bravery, Honesty, Humility and Truth. While these are broad Indigenous teachings, in Mi'kma'ki we have always had values and ways of living that were important to us. These include balance, honour, generosity, sharing, faith, hope, humour, strength, knowledge, respect for nature and elders, wisdom, and knowledge.

Our ways of living included the importance of planning with the seasons of the year. This allowed us to be proactive to ensure good living for our people. Today, it is still important to be proactive in planning ahead, whether it is for the season or the year.

As part of this, it is also important to set your intentions and reset the energy you want to bring forward. We are able to move beyond survival and focus on how we want to be or feel. Sometimes when life gets busy, our wellbeing gets put to the backburner and we neglect our own needs. By taking time to reflect and plan ahead, we put our wellbeing as a priority and enable ourselves to live our best life.

The power is within you to live full circle.

How to use this Planner
Your Medicine Wheel and Annual Plan

Growing to our fullest potential in each quadrant allows us to live our best life and to live full circle. Recognizing areas that need improvement allows greater self-awareness and opportunity to focus our attention where it is needed.

The directions start from the east.
This is the direction from (Mi'kmaq) keepers of the eastern door.

East direction is physical (yellow)   South direction is mental (blue)

West direction is emotional (red)   North direction is spiritual (white)

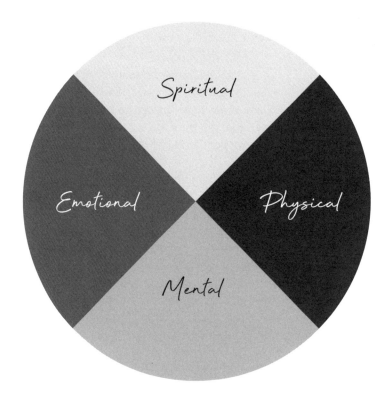

How do you feel about yourself in each area? How do you behave in each area?

Physical:

Emotional:

Mental:

Spiritual:

On a scale from 0-10, how strong do you feel in each quadrant?

Physical:

Emotional:

Mental:

Spiritual:

What is working well? What is missing or needs improvement?

Physical:

Emotional:

Mental:

Spiritual:

Reflect holistically on where you are and where you want to be this time next year.
Let the reflections of the medicine wheel guide and focus your goals for the year ahead.
Take the time to reset your energy and intentions in order to strengthen all areas of your
life and start living full circle. Review and adjust often.

SOME EXAMPLES OF BALANCE IN THESE AREAS CAN INCLUDE:

⊗ **East | Physical** – Physical wellness, movement and energy (others include presence, sleep, relaxation, routine, action, exercise, hobbies)

⊗ **South | Mental** – Honesty with self and others (others include intellect, career, education, wisdom, leadership, play, read, journal, meditation, calm)

⊗ **West | Emotional** – Joy, creativity, home environment and others (others include self-talk, confidence, acceptance, beliefs, expectations, laughing, sharing, singing, art, visiting, feeling content or at peace with self)

⊗ **North | Spiritual** – Relationship with self and others (others include gratitude, seeing your beauty, enlightenment, resiliency, mindfulness, connections, belonging, smudging, praying)

Annual Reflection & Planning

Reflect on the past year and use the layouts to fill in your notable accomplishments and successes. Use the teachings of the Medicine Wheel to set a strategic life plan. Assess goals for the four key aspects of your life including:

PHYSICAL | BODY (doing, fun, recreation, singing, dancing, rest, physical health, healthy eating)

MENTAL | MIND (thinking, stress management, resiliency, professional satisfaction)

EMOTIONAL | HEART (feeling, family, friends, significant other)

SPIRITUAL | CONNECTING (experiencing, culture, tradition, nurturing spirit)

How balanced is your wheel? What areas need more attention to achieve greater balance in your life?

Physical:

Mental:

Emotional:

Spiritual:

My Year in Review

My Year in Review

Where are you now? Identify your accomplishments

PROFESSIONAL

FINANCIAL

PERSONAL

HEALTH

EDUCATION

SPIRITUAL

OTHER

What is working?
What did you learn about yourself?

What do you no longer want in your life?
What are some boundaries that you could benefit from?

Your life vision: Ultimately, what do you want your life to look like?

Your legacy: How do you want to be remembered by future generations? What do you want to be known for?

Theme Word of the Year

Based on reviewing your medicine wheel, what word serves your spirit and garners your focus? For example, I have used: nurture, calm and connection. During the years of using each of those words, that is what my spirit needed most. Take time to reflect on one word that you want for yourself and to focus this year.

Where do you want to be in 5 years? How do you want to feel?
What does success look like to you?

What values are most important to you?

List your goals in each area

PROFESSIONAL

FINANCIAL

PERSONAL

HEALTH

EDUCATION

SPIRITUAL

OTHER

Achieving your Goals

GOAL SETTING

A goal is something you want to achieve. In looking at your values, vision, and the legacy you want to leave, boundaries you want to set, and what you want to accomplish for the year ahead, highlight key goals that you want to aim for. Keep these goals as big, high-level goals and work to break them down into SMART goals.

SMART GOALS

Reflect on the last page with all you want to accomplish and identify 4 key goals you want to achieve this year. These will be your key goals to work on.

SPECIFIC — well defined and clear

MEASURABLE — how you will measure progress towards accomplishing your goal

ACHIEVABLE — possible to achieve

REALISTIC — within reach and relevant to your intentions

TIMELY — clearly defined timeline that has start and end dates

SMART goals were developed by George Doran, Arthur Miller and James Cunningham in their 1981 article "There's a S.M.A.R.T. way to write management goals and objectives"

Key Goal 1:

Purpose of this goal

Possible challenges/solutions

Other people to include

Keydates & Timeframe

Actions to take

_____ ○
_____ ○
_____ ○
_____ ○
_____ ○

Key Goal 2:

Purpose of this goal

Possible challenges/solutions

Other people to include

Keydates & Timeframe

Actions to take

_____ ○
_____ ○
_____ ○
_____ ○
_____ ○

SMART GOALS ✓ SPECIFIC ✓ MEASURABLE ✓ ACHIEVABLE ✓ REALISTIC ✓ TIMELY

Key Goal 3:

Purpose of this goal

Possible challenges/solutions

Other people to include

Keydates & Timeframe

Actions to take

_____ ○
_____ ○
_____ ○
_____ ○
_____ ○

Key Goal 4:

Purpose of this goal

Possible challenges/solutions

Other people to include

Keydates & Timeframe

Actions to take

_____ ○
_____ ○
_____ ○
_____ ○
_____ ○

SMART GOALS   ✓ SPECIFIC   ✓ MEASURABLE   ✓ ACHIEVABLE   ✓ REALISTIC   ✓ TIMELY

Self-Reflection:

SETTING THE TONE FOR YOUR YEAR AHEAD.

Self-Reflection:

What are your passions?

What are your strengths?

What are your weaknesses?

Where can you leverage more time? (ie. driving, early morning, etc)

How can you live fully?

How can you improve your mornings, afternoons, evenings?

What can you do to leave the world a better place?

What would it look like to act the way you want to feel?

What are 10 things you need to function at your best? (ex. Early to bed, 1 hour of alone time each day, etc)

Monthly Inspirational Theme & Planning

FOCUS FOR THE MONTH AHEAD

At the first of each month, take time to go back and look at your weekly accomplishments – take a breath and celebrate those wins! Great job. How does it feel to be able to look back on those four weeks and acknowledge your wins?

Each monthly layout includes a to-do list, a to-be list, current opportunities to explore, actions that will serve your legacy and important events, as well as a full month undated layout Sunday to Saturday.

This space is for you to plan what you want to do, achieve, and how you want to be!

Weekly Reflection & Planning

ALIGN YOUR HEART AND MIND

I can be guilty of spending a lot of time in my head and it takes effort on my part to avoid going to planning or fix-it mode. Sometimes I avoid sitting with my feelings at all costs! The medicine wheel framework I use supports me in looking inward in a wholistic way to identifying what I need to achieve greater balance and healing. Once I identify my needs and make the effort to avoid the noise around me and acknowledge my feelings that I don't necessarily want to feel, then I feel grounded again.

You may have been here too. Shopping, working or eating to avoid feelings. Ignoring your body, ignoring your intuition, putting up a wall between your heart and head and trying to avoid feeling sad, mad and disappointed. These are natural aspects of being human and when you accept, instead of avoid, your feelings, they end up teaching you about yourself.

HOW YOU WANT TO FEEL

I included a section each day on *"How I want to feel"* to provide daily opportunity for consideration. By bringing this to our attention each day, we are more apt to reflect on it, and hopefully guide our actions towards how we want to feel. Too often we are focusing on things outside of ourselves, but the real change starts within.

To achieve well-being, you must connect your thoughts and feelings. This connection is mutually dependent. Ever notice how stressful thoughts lead to pain in your shoulder or neck? That's a common symptom for me. It is a sign my body needs attention and I am lacking balance. These are symptoms of being unbalanced. To address this, we must look inwards and determine how we want to feel and what needs to be reduced or incorporated to achieve greater balance. For this reason, the planner includes a space to write down 'How I want to feel'!

Identifying how you want to feel is just as important as identifying what you want to do each day. Identifying how you want to feel on a particular day allows you to focus on that area.

Some days I know that it is important for me to place extra attention on remaining calm or staying focused. Where this extra energy is needed varies on certain days.

Do you want to feel happy, calm, energized, determined, focused, strong, independent, grateful? This planner gives you the space to note what you need most each day.

GRATITUDE

What are you grateful for in your life? Expressing gratitude is key to improving mindset and reflecting on what is important in your world. It takes our thoughts away from negativity and guides us towards focusing on the good. There are so many things to be thankful for including your health, safety, nature, family, friends and so on. You can express appreciation for things big or small. This gives you an opportunity to focus on what you have instead of what you lack, which is important in establishing a healthy mindset, and leads to greater fulfillment. I incorporate this practice into my daily life, and it has made me realize how many things I have to be thankful for. It allows me to acknowledge my joy.

Write down what you are grateful for every week. Reflect on each quadrant of the medicine wheel and write down your gratitudes within each one. There are some days when it isn't as easy to acknowledge all the good that surrounds us. These are the days when expressing our gratitude helps most in our healing journey. The more we incorporate this practice, the more aware we become of the many gifts we have in life.

4 BIG GOALS

A goal is something you want or wish to achieve.
A task is the work that needs to be completed to achieve your goal.
Each week you have the opportunity to outline 4 big goals that you want to work towards, and includes the tasks you need to complete to achieve those goals.

Setting four big goals for the week improves your focus on what is important for the week. Take the time to set these big goals at the first of the week. Your goals align your focus on how you are going to spend your energy and time for the week. In a world that demands your attention in so many areas, it is really important for you to identify what is truly important for you to spend your energy on. Setting goals helps keep you accountable, encourages you to take action and helps you live your best life with clear focus. Remember, SMART goals are:

Specific - well defined and clear
Measurable - how you will measure progress towards accomplishing your goal
Achievable - possible to achieve
Realistic - within reach and relevant to your intentions
Timely - clearly defined timeline that has start and end dates

Having SMART goals help to bridge the gap between intentions and actions.

TASKS

Set tasks from your big goals for the week. These tasks can be broken down into manageable steps from your SMART goals. What actions need to be taken to achieve your goal?

Writing down tasks signals and reminds you of actions that need to be completed. Prioritize your tasks. What is urgent? What is important? Once complete, check them off!

HABIT TRACKING

Writing down habits helps you to identify what you want to instill in your life to become a better version of yourself. Repetition helps with instilling habits in your life. In the weekly layout, there is a habit chart. This chart enables you to track habits that are important for your mindset, wellness and routine. For me, key habits include going to bed early, a daily 30-minute walk, water intake, limiting technology after 8pm and daily affirmations. These are all important to me and what I want to focus on tracking daily.

What are some habits you can track? How will they improve your life?

Habits become effortless with planning, ease and repetition. The easier you make habits for yourself the more you will succeed; it's the path of least resistance. Some examples are setting out your favourite water bottle, setting reminder alarms, planning the time of your daily walk, and leaving your walking shoes, clothes or equipment in a convenient location. Plan ahead on how you want your week to look.

"A little progress every day adds up to big results" - Satya Nani

NOTES

Each week there is space for you to write out notes for your personal or professional life. I enjoy writing things out, and writing things down has always helped me solidify important information. Use colourful pens and make it fun!

WEEKLY SUCCESS AND ACCOMPLISHMENTS

While you are dedicated to accomplishing your goals and tasks, it is important to take time to reflect on your success! It shocked me when I started doing this and was able to look back and see what I had achieved. Without having them written down, I'm sure I would have forgotten how much I had to celebrate.

This journey is about you! Learning to live with balance and intention includes celebrating your success and growth. Your growth means you are changing for the better. It's important to track that. When you reflect on your medicine wheel, how you feel physically, mentally, spiritually and emotionally may be different as you incorporate this framework of reflection over the year.

Quick tip: You will find quick tips throughout the journal in the monthly reflections. Use this planner every day for scheduling, how you want to feel, notes, tracking progress on tasks and habits. At the first of each week plan ahead with your 4 big goals and outline the tasks required to accomplish those goals. At the end of the week track successes and take time to reflect on your week and what needs to be brought forward to next week.

Take five minutes every morning to just be, breathe and be with yourself.
Think of the following questions and add your reflections to the weekly layout:

Today I am grateful for...

Today I am letting go of....

Today I want to be...

Indigenous Sacred Teachings:

Love   Honesty   Humility   Respect   Truth   Patience   Wisdom

"Never separate the life you live from the words you speak." – Paul Wellstone

All of these are interconnected and guide your actions. They are the seven gifts of life to live in a good way. The late Mi'kmaw Elder, Dr. Murdena Marshall, spoke of these gifts and said that if all of these gifts were visible in a person, that person is an Elder.

 *Takeaways*

What would it look like to live your life according to these teachings?

Actions speak louder than words.

How will you become better every day?

Quick tip: Writing down your goals outlines what you want to work towards; it takes action to achieve them!

Focus for the upcoming month

Current opportunities to explore

Actions that will serve my legacy

Important events

NOTES

MONTH:　　　　　　　　**WEEK:**

Monday	**Tuesday**	**Wednesday**
How I want to feel today:	How I want to feel today:	How I want to feel today:

GOALS

- _____
- _____
- _____
- _____

TASKS

- _____
- _____
- _____
- _____
- _____
- _____
- _____
- _____
- _____
- _____
- _____
- _____

NOTES

"I think the inspiration to do these things comes down to love. Love of the land, and love of the people – and that's the basis of all of it." – Helen Knott, Author

Thursday
How I want to feel today:

☼

_____
_____
_____
_____
_____

☼

_____
_____
_____
_____
_____

☾

_____
_____
_____
_____

Friday
How I want to feel today:

☼

_____
_____
_____
_____
_____

☼

_____
_____
_____
_____
_____

☾

_____
_____
_____
_____

Saturday
How I want to feel today:

_____
_____
_____
_____
_____

Sunday
How I want to feel today:

_____
_____
_____
_____
_____

Weekly Highlights & Successes

GRATITUDE LIST

_____
_____
_____
_____
_____
_____
_____

HABIT TRACKER

1 · _____
2 · _____
3 · _____
4 · _____
5 · _____
6 · _____
7 · _____

M	T	W	T	F	S	S
○	○	○	○	○	○	○
○	○	○	○	○	○	○
○	○	○	○	○	○	○
○	○	○	○	○	○	○
○	○	○	○	○	○	○
○	○	○	○	○	○	○
○	○	○	○	○	○	○

MONTH:

WEEK:

Monday
How I want to feel today:

Tuesday
How I want to feel today:

Wednesday
How I want to feel today:

GOALS

TASKS

☼

☼

☼

☀

☀

☀

☾

☾

☾

NOTES

"Bullying, jealousy, hate, greed, lies, arrogance, searing self-absorption, destructive 'power over' mentalities are wasteful pursuits and causes the human heart to fall to the ground. It is beyond healing, beyond human conscience when women fight with each other. We are Mother Earth's heartbeat, it is our responsibility to bring peace, harmony and balance back to the world. This will not happen if we continue to find fault with ourselves and perpetuate it on our sisters." - Shannon Thunderbird, Tsimshian singer and storyteller

Thursday	Friday	Saturday	Weekly Highlights & Successes
How I want to feel today:	How I want to feel today:	How I want to feel today:	

☼

☼

_____

_____

_____

_____

_____

☀

☀

Sunday

How I want to feel today:

_____

_____

_____

_____

☾

☾

GRATITUDE LIST

_____

_____

_____

_____

_____

_____

_____

HABIT TRACKER

1 · _____
2 · _____
3 · _____
4 · _____
5 · _____
6 · _____
7 · _____

M	T	W	T	F	S	S
○	○	○	○	○	○	○
○	○	○	○	○	○	○
○	○	○	○	○	○	○
○	○	○	○	○	○	○
○	○	○	○	○	○	○
○	○	○	○	○	○	○
○	○	○	○	○	○	○

MONTH:　　　　　　　　**WEEK:**

Monday
How I want to feel today:

Tuesday
How I want to feel today:

Wednesday
How I want to feel today:

GOALS

- _____
- _____
- _____
- _____

TASKS

- _____
- _____
- _____
- _____
- _____
- _____
- _____
- _____
- _____
- _____
- _____

☼

☼

☼

◐

◐

◐

☾

☾

☾

NOTES

"You only have one life to live. Your life will be what you make it." – Elder Carolyn Sark

Thursday
How I want to feel today:

☼

_____
_____
_____
_____
_____

☀

_____
_____
_____
_____
_____

☽

_____
_____
_____
_____

Friday
How I want to feel today:

☼

_____
_____
_____
_____
_____

☀

_____
_____
_____
_____
_____

☽

_____
_____
_____
_____

Saturday
How I want to feel today:

_____
_____
_____
_____
_____

Sunday
How I want to feel today:

_____
_____
_____
_____
_____
_____

Weekly Highlights & Successes

GRATITUDE LIST

_____
_____
_____
_____
_____
_____

HABIT TRACKER

1 • _____
2 • _____
3 • _____
4 • _____
5 • _____
6 • _____
7 • _____

M	T	W	T	F	S	S
○	○	○	○	○	○	○
○	○	○	○	○	○	○
○	○	○	○	○	○	○
○	○	○	○	○	○	○
○	○	○	○	○	○	○
○	○	○	○	○	○	○
○	○	○	○	○	○	○

MONTH:

WEEK:

Monday
How I want to feel today:

Tuesday
How I want to feel today:

Wednesday
How I want to feel today:

GOALS

TASKS

NOTES

"Language and culture cannot be separated. Language is vital to understanding our unique cultural perspectives. Language is a tool that is used to explore and experience our cultures and the perspectives that are embedded in our cultures." - Buffy Sainte-Marie

Thursday
How I want to feel today:

☼

_____
_____
_____
_____
_____
_____

☀

_____
_____
_____
_____
_____
_____

☾

_____
_____
_____
_____

Friday
How I want to feel today:

☼

_____
_____
_____
_____
_____
_____

☀

_____
_____
_____
_____
_____
_____

☾

_____
_____
_____
_____

Saturday
How I want to feel today:

_____
_____
_____
_____
_____
_____

Sunday
How I want to feel today:

_____
_____
_____
_____
_____
_____
_____

Weekly Highlights & Successes

GRATITUDE LIST

_____
_____
_____
_____
_____
_____

HABIT TRACKER

1 • _____
2 • _____
3 • _____
4 • _____
5 • _____
6 • _____
7 • _____

M	T	W	T	F	S	S
○	○	○	○	○	○	○
○	○	○	○	○	○	○
○	○	○	○	○	○	○
○	○	○	○	○	○	○
○	○	○	○	○	○	○
○	○	○	○	○	○	○
○	○	○	○	○	○	○

Prioritize Your Goals.

"Everyone thinks of changing the world, but no one thinks of changing himself."
- Leo Tolstoy

Your focus is the gateway of your thoughts. If you want success in what you are working towards, keep your eye on the prize and don't get distracted by potential obstacles that could draw your attention from what you are trying to achieve.

 *Takeaways*

How can you simplify things in your life?

What can you do to gain clarity on your priorities?

What can you let go of that is no longer serving you?

Quick tip: Your focus determines your reality.

Focus for the upcoming month

Current opportunities to explore

Actions that will serve my legacy

Important events

NOTES

MONTH: **WEEK:**

Monday
How I want to feel today:

Tuesday
How I want to feel today:

Wednesday
How I want to feel today:

GOALS

- _____
- _____
- _____
- _____

TASKS

- _____
- _____
- _____
- _____
- _____
- _____
- _____
- _____
- _____
- _____
- _____
- _____
- _____

NOTES

"No matter what anyone else is doing, what I am doing is about positive love and to show that we can, as Indigenous people, create our own economies." - Jenn Harper, Founder and Owner Cheekbone Beauty

Thursday	**Friday**	**Saturday**	**Weekly Highlights & Successes**

Thursday
How I want to feel today:

☼
_____
_____
_____
_____
_____

☀
_____
_____
_____
_____
_____

☾
_____
_____
_____
_____

Friday
How I want to feel today:

☼
_____
_____
_____
_____
_____

☀
_____
_____
_____
_____
_____

☾
_____
_____
_____
_____

Saturday
How I want to feel today:

_____
_____
_____
_____
_____
_____

Sunday
How I want to feel today:

_____
_____
_____
_____

GRATITUDE LIST

_____
_____
_____
_____
_____
_____
_____

HABIT TRACKER

1 • _____
2 • _____
3 • _____
4 • _____
5 • _____
6 • _____
7 • _____

M	T	W	T	F	S	S
○	○	○	○	○	○	○
○	○	○	○	○	○	○
○	○	○	○	○	○	○
○	○	○	○	○	○	○
○	○	○	○	○	○	○
○	○	○	○	○	○	○
○	○	○	○	○	○	○

MONTH:

WEEK:

Monday
How I want to feel today:

Tuesday
How I want to feel today:

Wednesday
How I want to feel today:

GOALS

TASKS

NOTES

"My story may be rooted in trauma but it's not my only story."
Elaine Alec -Author of "Calling My Spirit Back"

Thursday
How I want to feel today:

☼

_____
_____
_____
_____
_____
_____

☼

_____
_____
_____
_____
_____
_____

☾

_____
_____
_____
_____

Friday
How I want to feel today:

☼

_____
_____
_____
_____
_____
_____

☼

_____
_____
_____
_____
_____
_____

☾

_____
_____
_____
_____

Saturday
How I want to feel today:

_____
_____
_____
_____
_____
_____

Sunday
How I want to feel today:

_____
_____
_____
_____
_____

Weekly Highlights & Successes

GRATITUDE LIST

_____
_____
_____
_____
_____
_____
_____

HABIT TRACKER

1 • _____
2 • _____
3 • _____
4 • _____
5 • _____
6 • _____
7 • _____

M	T	W	T	F	S	S
○	○	○	○	○	○	○
○	○	○	○	○	○	○
○	○	○	○	○	○	○
○	○	○	○	○	○	○
○	○	○	○	○	○	○
○	○	○	○	○	○	○
○	○	○	○	○	○	○

MONTH:

WEEK:

Monday
How I want to feel today:

Tuesday
How I want to feel today:

Wednesday
How I want to feel today:

GOALS

TASKS

☼

☼

☼

☾

☾

☾

NOTES

"Nothing's impossible. It's what you decide your limits are." – Lori Ann Muenzer, Olympic gold medalist

Thursday
How I want to feel today:

☀

_____
_____
_____
_____
_____
_____

☼

_____
_____
_____
_____
_____
_____

☾

_____
_____
_____
_____

Friday
How I want to feel today:

☀

_____
_____
_____
_____
_____
_____

☼

_____
_____
_____
_____
_____
_____

☾

_____
_____
_____
_____

Saturday
How I want to feel today:

_____
_____
_____
_____
_____
_____

Sunday
How I want to feel today:

_____
_____
_____
_____
_____
_____

Weekly Highlights & Successes

GRATITUDE LIST

_____
_____
_____
_____
_____
_____
_____

HABIT TRACKER

1 • _____
2 • _____
3 • _____
4 • _____
5 • _____
6 • _____
7 • _____

M	T	W	T	F	S	S
○	○	○	○	○	○	○
○	○	○	○	○	○	○
○	○	○	○	○	○	○
○	○	○	○	○	○	○
○	○	○	○	○	○	○
○	○	○	○	○	○	○
○	○	○	○	○	○	○

MONTH:

WEEK:

Monday
How I want to feel today:

Tuesday
How I want to feel today:

Wednesday
How I want to feel today:

GOALS

○ _____
○ _____
○ _____
○ _____

TASKS

○ _____
○ _____
○ _____
○ _____
○ _____
○ _____
○ _____
○ _____
○ _____
○ _____
○ _____
○ _____

☼

☼

☼

◐

◐

◐

☾

☾

☾

NOTES

"Obviously I enjoy being well received or successful, but my goals aren't for other people to know about, they're for me."
– Lynn Crawford

Thursday	**Friday**	**Saturday**	**Weekly Highlights & Successes**

Thursday
How I want to feel today:

☼
_____
_____
_____
_____
_____
_____

◐
_____
_____
_____
_____
_____
_____

☾
_____
_____
_____
_____

Friday
How I want to feel today:

☼
_____
_____
_____
_____
_____
_____

◐
_____
_____
_____
_____
_____
_____

☾
_____
_____
_____
_____

Saturday
How I want to feel today:

_____
_____
_____
_____
_____
_____

Sunday
How I want to feel today:

_____
_____
_____
_____
_____
_____
_____

Weekly Highlights & Successes

GRATITUDE LIST

_____
_____
_____
_____
_____
_____

HABIT TRACKER

1 • _____
2 • _____
3 • _____
4 • _____
5 • _____
6 • _____
7 • _____

M	T	W	T	F	S	S
○	○	○	○	○	○	○
○	○	○	○	○	○	○
○	○	○	○	○	○	○
○	○	○	○	○	○	○
○	○	○	○	○	○	○
○	○	○	○	○	○	○
○	○	○	○	○	○	○

Balancing Work with Life.

"Energy flows where intentions go."

Be conscious of the energy of balance. When you focus on balance, your energy is drawn to what is needed. Create balance with boundaries in all aspects of your life – physically, mentally, emotionally and spiritual. Balance and boundaries are daily practices that should be incorporated at home and at work.

 *Takeaways*

What are tasks you could delegate, that are a poor use of your time, or that diminish your happiness?

What can you do to prioritize your family time?

Are there areas in your life where boundaries need to be set?

Quick tip: Start by identifying boundaries that are non-negotiable.

Focus for the upcoming month

Current opportunities to explore

Actions that will serve my legacy

Important events

NOTES

MONTH:

WEEK:

Monday
How I want to feel today:

Tuesday
How I want to feel today:

Wednesday
How I want to feel today:

GOALS

- _____
- _____
- _____
- _____

TASKS

- _____
- _____
- _____
- _____
- _____
- _____
- _____
- _____
- _____
- _____
- _____
- _____

NOTES

"You have to leave room in life to dream." - Buffy Sainte-Marie

Thursday
How I want to feel today:

☼
_____
_____
_____
_____
_____
_____

☀
_____
_____
_____
_____
_____
_____

☾
_____
_____
_____
_____

Friday
How I want to feel today:

☼
_____
_____
_____
_____
_____
_____

☀
_____
_____
_____
_____
_____
_____

☾
_____
_____
_____
_____

Saturday
How I want to feel today:

_____
_____

Sunday
How I want to feel today:

_____
_____
_____
_____
_____
_____

Weekly Highlights & Successes

GRATITUDE LIST

_____
_____
_____
_____
_____
_____
_____

HABIT TRACKER

1 · _____
2 · _____
3 · _____
4 · _____
5 · _____
6 · _____
7 · _____

M	T	W	T	F	S	S
○	○	○	○	○	○	○
○	○	○	○	○	○	○
○	○	○	○	○	○	○
○	○	○	○	○	○	○
○	○	○	○	○	○	○
○	○	○	○	○	○	○
○	○	○	○	○	○	○

MONTH: **WEEK:**

Monday
How I want to feel today:

Tuesday
How I want to feel today:

Wednesday
How I want to feel today:

GOALS

TASKS

NOTES

"Don't ever let anyone tell you that you cannot go through a particular door. Always be prepared to go through a door that leads to your goal." - Ann Saddlemyer, scholar

Thursday
How I want to feel today:

☼

_____
_____
_____
_____
_____
_____

☀

_____
_____
_____
_____
_____
_____

☾

_____
_____
_____
_____

Friday
How I want to feel today:

☼

_____
_____
_____
_____
_____
_____

☀

_____
_____
_____
_____
_____
_____

☾

_____
_____
_____
_____

Saturday
How I want to feel today:

_____
_____
_____
_____
_____
_____

Sunday
How I want to feel today:

_____
_____
_____
_____
_____
_____

Weekly Highlights & Successes

GRATITUDE LIST

_____
_____
_____
_____
_____
_____
_____

HABIT TRACKER

1 · _____
2 · _____
3 · _____
4 · _____
5 · _____
6 · _____
7 · _____

M	T	W	T	F	S	S
○	○	○	○	○	○	○
○	○	○	○	○	○	○
○	○	○	○	○	○	○
○	○	○	○	○	○	○
○	○	○	○	○	○	○
○	○	○	○	○	○	○
○	○	○	○	○	○	○

Living
FULL CIRCLE

MONTH:

WEEK:

Monday
How I want to feel today:

Tuesday
How I want to feel today:

Wednesday
How I want to feel today:

GOALS

TASKS

NOTES

> "I see a peaceful world in which we have finally come to terms with the reality that our survival depends on abandoning conflict, working for peace, sharing what we have and living within our ecological means." - Elizabeth May, environmentalist

Thursday
How I want to feel today:

☀

_____
_____
_____
_____
_____

☀☽

_____
_____
_____
_____
_____

☾

_____
_____
_____
_____

Friday
How I want to feel today:

☀

_____
_____
_____
_____
_____

☀☽

_____
_____
_____
_____
_____

☾

_____
_____
_____
_____

Saturday
How I want to feel today:

_____
_____
_____
_____
_____

Sunday
How I want to feel today:

_____
_____
_____
_____
_____

Weekly Highlights & Successes

GRATITUDE LIST

_____
_____
_____
_____
_____
_____
_____

HABIT TRACKER

1 • _____
2 • _____
3 • _____
4 • _____
5 • _____
6 • _____
7 • _____

M	T	W	T	F	S	S
○	○	○	○	○	○	○
○	○	○	○	○	○	○
○	○	○	○	○	○	○
○	○	○	○	○	○	○
○	○	○	○	○	○	○
○	○	○	○	○	○	○
○	○	○	○	○	○	○

MONTH:

WEEK:

Monday
How I want to feel today:

Tuesday
How I want to feel today:

Wednesday
How I want to feel today.

GOALS

- _____
- _____
- _____
- _____

TASKS

- _____
- _____
- _____
- _____
- _____
- _____
- _____
- _____
- _____
- _____
- _____
- _____

NOTES

"Words don't change children's lives. Real action by the government and equality would."
- Cindy Blackstock

Thursday

How I want to feel today:

☼

_____
_____
_____
_____
_____

☼̣

_____
_____
_____
_____
_____

☾

_____
_____
_____
_____

Friday

How I want to feel today:

☼

_____
_____
_____
_____
_____

☼̣

_____
_____
_____
_____
_____

☾

_____
_____
_____
_____

Saturday

How I want to feel today:

_____
_____
_____
_____
_____

Sunday

How I want to feel today:

_____
_____
_____
_____
_____

Weekly Highlights & Successes

GRATITUDE LIST

_____
_____
_____
_____
_____
_____
_____

HABIT TRACKER

1 • _____
2 • _____
3 • _____
4 • _____
5 • _____
6 • _____
7 • _____

M	T	W	T	F	S	S
○	○	○	○	○	○	○
○	○	○	○	○	○	○
○	○	○	○	○	○	○
○	○	○	○	○	○	○
○	○	○	○	○	○	○
○	○	○	○	○	○	○
○	○	○	○	○	○	○

Living
FULL CIRCLE

Routines to Create Your Best Life.

"Do your best and let life do the rest." - Robin Sharma

Create even more balance with routine. When you create a routine, you identify what you want to do and make it a part of your schedule. Increasing productivity through routine maximizes your day and gets you to your goals faster.

 *Takeaways*

How can you use time to the best of your advantage?

What are some easy routines you can incorporate?

How can you include an activity into your routine to help ground you?

Quick tip: Harness your best hours to maximize your productivity.

Focus for the upcoming month

Current opportunities to explore

Actions that will serve my legacy

Important events

NOTES

Living
FULL CIRCLE

MONTH: **WEEK:**

Monday	**Tuesday**	**Wednesday**
How I want to feel today:	How I want to feel today:	How I want to feel today:

GOALS

- _____
- _____
- _____
- _____

TASKS

- _____
- _____
- _____
- _____
- _____
- _____
- _____
- _____
- _____
- _____
- _____
- _____

☼

☀

☾

NOTES

Thursday
How I want to feel today:

☼

_____
_____
_____
_____

☀

_____
_____
_____
_____

☾

_____
_____
_____

Friday
How I want to feel today:

☼

_____
_____
_____
_____

☀

_____
_____
_____
_____

☾

_____
_____
_____

Saturday
How I want to feel today:

_____
_____
_____
_____
_____

Sunday
How I want to feel today:

_____
_____
_____
_____
_____

Weekly Highlights & Successes

GRATITUDE LIST

_____
_____
_____
_____
_____
_____
_____

HABIT TRACKER

1 · _____
2 · _____
3 · _____
4 · _____
5 · _____
6 · _____
7 · _____

M	T	W	T	F	S	S
○	○	○	○	○	○	○
○	○	○	○	○	○	○
○	○	○	○	○	○	○
○	○	○	○	○	○	○
○	○	○	○	○	○	○
○	○	○	○	○	○	○
○	○	○	○	○	○	○

MONTH: WEEK:

Monday
How I want to feel today:

Tuesday
How I want to feel today:

Wednesday
How I want to feel today:

GOALS

TASKS

NOTES

> "If you're careful to listen to your instincts and question conventional wisdom, set priorities, and make thoughtful choices, eventually you will figure out how to design a lifestyle that suits you." - Arlene Dickinson, businesswoman and television personality

Thursday
How I want to feel today:

☼

_____
_____
_____
_____
_____

☼̇

_____
_____
_____
_____

☾

_____
_____
_____
_____

Friday
How I want to feel today:

☼

_____
_____
_____
_____
_____

☼̇

_____
_____
_____
_____

☾

_____
_____
_____
_____

Saturday
How I want to feel today:

_____
_____
_____
_____

Sunday
How I want to feel today:

_____
_____
_____
_____
_____
_____

Weekly Highlights & Successes

GRATITUDE LIST

_____
_____
_____
_____
_____
_____

HABIT TRACKER

1 • _____
2 • _____
3 • _____
4 • _____
5 • _____
6 • _____
7 • _____

M	T	W	T	F	S	S
○	○	○	○	○	○	○
○	○	○	○	○	○	○
○	○	○	○	○	○	○
○	○	○	○	○	○	○
○	○	○	○	○	○	○
○	○	○	○	○	○	○
○	○	○	○	○	○	○

MONTH:

WEEK:

Monday
How I want to feel today:

Tuesday
How I want to feel today:

Wednesday
How I want to feel today:

GOALS

_____
_____
_____
_____

TASKS

_____
_____
_____
_____
_____
_____
_____
_____
_____
_____
_____
_____

☀
_____
_____
_____
_____
_____

🌗
_____
_____
_____
_____

🌙
_____
_____
_____

☀
_____
_____
_____
_____
_____

🌗
_____
_____
_____
_____

🌙
_____
_____
_____

☀
_____
_____
_____
_____
_____

🌗
_____
_____
_____
_____

🌙
_____
_____
_____

NOTES

"We must open the doors and we must see to it they remain open, so that others can pass through." - Rosemary Brown

Thursday
How I want to feel today:

☼

_____
_____
_____
_____
_____

◐

_____
_____
_____
_____
_____

☾

_____
_____
_____
_____

Friday
How I want to feel today:

☼

_____
_____
_____
_____
_____

◐

_____
_____
_____
_____
_____

☾

_____
_____
_____
_____

Saturday
How I want to feel today:

_____
_____
_____
_____
_____

Sunday
How I want to feel today:

_____
_____
_____
_____
_____
_____
_____

Weekly Highlights & Successes

GRATITUDE LIST

_____
_____
_____
_____
_____
_____
_____

HABIT TRACKER

1 • _____
2 • _____
3 • _____
4 • _____
5 • _____
6 • _____
7 • _____

M	T	W	T	F	S	S
○	○	○	○	○	○	○
○	○	○	○	○	○	○
○	○	○	○	○	○	○
○	○	○	○	○	○	○
○	○	○	○	○	○	○
○	○	○	○	○	○	○
○	○	○	○	○	○	○

MONTH:

WEEK:

Monday
How I want to feel today:

Tuesday
How I want to feel today:

Wednesday
How I want to feel today:

GOALS

- _____
- _____
- _____
- _____

TASKS

- _____
- _____
- _____
- _____
- _____
- _____
- _____
- _____
- _____
- _____
- _____
- _____

NOTES

"Does it pay to listen? Always." – Arlene Dickinson, businesswoman and television personality

Thursday
How I want to feel today:

☼
_____
_____
_____
_____
_____
_____

☀
_____
_____
_____
_____
_____
_____

☾
_____
_____
_____
_____

Friday
How I want to feel today:

☼
_____
_____
_____
_____
_____
_____

☀
_____
_____
_____
_____
_____
_____

☾
_____
_____
_____
_____

Saturday
How I want to feel today:

_____
_____
_____
_____
_____
_____
_____

Sunday
How I want to feel today:

_____
_____
_____
_____
_____
_____

Weekly Highlights & Successes

GRATITUDE LIST

_____
_____
_____
_____
_____
_____
_____

HABIT TRACKER

1 • _____
2 • _____
3 • _____
4 • _____
5 • _____
6 • _____
7 • _____

M	T	W	T	F	S	S
○	○	○	○	○	○	○
○	○	○	○	○	○	○
○	○	○	○	○	○	○
○	○	○	○	○	○	○
○	○	○	○	○	○	○
○	○	○	○	○	○	○
○	○	○	○	○	○	○

Simplify Your Life!

"No idea works until you do the work."- Robin Sharma

Simplifying your life means focusing on what is truly important to you. You can simplify your space, your schedule, your home, your mornings, your mind, your relationships – the possibilities are endless! Simplifying your life and what is truly important helps identify what is or isn't needed. This is an important part of ensuring balance and intentional living. Everything starts and ends within you.

 *Takeaways*

Describe your ideal space.

How will you develop habits to instill in your daily routine?

What can you discard? What can you organize?

Quick tip: Surround yourself with the things that you love and put things where they belong.

Focus for the upcoming month

Current opportunities to explore

Actions that will serve my legacy

Important events

NOTES

MONTH:　　　　　　　　　　**WEEK:**

Monday	**Tuesday**	**Wednesday**
How I want to feel today:	How I want to feel today:	How I want to feel today:

GOALS

○ _____
○ _____
○ _____
○ _____

TASKS

○ _____
○ _____
○ _____
○ _____
○ _____
○ _____
○ _____
○ _____
○ _____
○ _____
○ _____
○ _____
○ _____

☼

☼

☼

☼

☼

☼

☽

☽

☽

NOTES

"Even before you've earned it, treat yourself and your career with the level of respect that you hope to one day deserve."
– Catherine O'Hara, actress

Thursday
How I want to feel today:

☼

_____
_____
_____
_____
_____

☼

_____
_____
_____
_____
_____

☾

_____
_____
_____
_____

Friday
How I want to feel today:

☼

_____
_____
_____
_____
_____

☼

_____
_____
_____
_____
_____

☾

_____
_____
_____
_____

Saturday
How I want to feel today:

_____
_____
_____
_____
_____

Sunday
How I want to feel today:

_____
_____
_____
_____
_____

Weekly Highlights & Successes

GRATITUDE LIST

_____
_____
_____
_____
_____
_____
_____

HABIT TRACKER

1 • _____
2 • _____
3 • _____
4 • _____
5 • _____
6 • _____
7 • _____

M	T	W	T	F	S	S
○	○	○	○	○	○	○
○	○	○	○	○	○	○
○	○	○	○	○	○	○
○	○	○	○	○	○	○
○	○	○	○	○	○	○
○	○	○	○	○	○	○
○	○	○	○	○	○	○

MONTH:

WEEK:

Monday
How I want to feel today:

Tuesday
How I want to feel today:

Wednesday
How I want to feel today:

GOALS

TASKS

NOTES

"Take your voice to where it'll be most effective." – Buffy Sainte-Marie, singer-songwriter

Thursday
How I want to feel today:

☀

_____
_____
_____
_____
_____

◐

_____
_____
_____
_____
_____

☾

_____
_____
_____
_____

Friday
How I want to feel today:

☀

_____
_____
_____
_____
_____

◐

_____
_____
_____
_____
_____

☾

_____
_____
_____
_____

Saturday
How I want to feel today:

_____
_____
_____
_____
_____

Sunday
How I want to feel today:

_____
_____
_____
_____

Weekly Highlights & Successes

GRATITUDE LIST

_____
_____
_____
_____
_____
_____

HABIT TRACKER

1 • _____
2 • _____
3 • _____
4 • _____
5 • _____
6 • _____
7 • _____

M	T	W	T	F	S	S
○	○	○	○	○	○	○
○	○	○	○	○	○	○
○	○	○	○	○	○	○
○	○	○	○	○	○	○
○	○	○	○	○	○	○
○	○	○	○	○	○	○
○	○	○	○	○	○	○

MONTH:

WEEK:

GOALS

TASKS

Monday
How I want to feel today:

☼

☼

☾

Tuesday
How I want to feel today:

☼

☼

☾

Wednesday
How I want to feel today:

☼

☼

☾

NOTES

"It's difficult to learn from success. I've learned more from my mistakes." – Louise Penny, author

Thursday

How I want to feel today:

☼

_____
_____
_____
_____
_____

☀

_____
_____
_____
_____
_____

☾

_____
_____
_____
_____

Friday

How I want to feel today:

☼

_____
_____
_____
_____
_____

☀

_____
_____
_____
_____
_____

☾

_____
_____
_____
_____

Saturday

How I want to feel today:

_____
_____
_____
_____
_____
_____

Sunday

How I want to feel today:

_____
_____
_____
_____
_____

Weekly Highlights & Successes

GRATITUDE LIST

_____
_____
_____
_____
_____
_____
_____

HABIT TRACKER

1 • _____
2 • _____
3 • _____
4 • _____
5 • _____
6 • _____
7 • _____

M	T	W	T	F	S	S
○	○	○	○	○	○	○
○	○	○	○	○	○	○
○	○	○	○	○	○	○
○	○	○	○	○	○	○
○	○	○	○	○	○	○
○	○	○	○	○	○	○
○	○	○	○	○	○	○

MONTH: **WEEK:**

Monday
How I want to feel today:

Tuesday
How I want to feel today:

Wednesday
How I want to feel today:

GOALS

TASKS

NOTES

"Pay attention to yourself. Build on who you are. Become a whole person. Enjoy life."
– Andrea Bain, television host and author

Thursday
How I want to feel today:

☼

_____
_____
_____
_____
_____

☀

_____
_____
_____
_____
_____

☾

_____
_____
_____

Friday
How I want to feel today:

☼

_____
_____
_____
_____
_____

☀

_____
_____
_____
_____
_____

☾

_____
_____
_____

Saturday
How I want to feel today:

_____
_____
_____
_____
_____
_____
_____

Sunday
How I want to feel today:

_____
_____
_____
_____
_____

Weekly Highlights & Successes

GRATITUDE LIST

_____
_____
_____
_____
_____
_____

HABIT TRACKER

1 • _____
2 • _____
3 • _____
4 • _____
5 • _____
6 • _____
7 • _____

M	T	W	T	F	S	S
○	○	○	○	○	○	○
○	○	○	○	○	○	○
○	○	○	○	○	○	○
○	○	○	○	○	○	○
○	○	○	○	○	○	○
○	○	○	○	○	○	○
○	○	○	○	○	○	○

Living
FULL CIRCLE

Prioritizing Healthy Boundaries.

"Focus is about saying no." - Steve Jobs

Don Miguel Ruiz shares The Four Agreements as a best practice for how to live your life. These agreements are about you, as are the medicine wheel teachings.

The Four Agreements
1. Be impeccable with your word
2. Don't take anything personally
3. Don't make assumptions
4. Always do your best

- Don Miguel Ruiz

 *Takeaways*

What distractions can you minimize in your life?

How can you surround yourself with those who you aspire to be?

What are some things that you want to say no to?

What can you change to live within your means?

Quick tip: Setting boundaries is a gift you give yourself.

Focus for the upcoming month

Current opportunities to explore

Actions that will serve my legacy

Important events

NOTES

MONTH: **WEEK:**

Monday
How I want to feel today:

Tuesday
How I want to feel today:

Wednesday
How I want to feel today:

GOALS

TASKS

NOTES

"We limit what we set out to do by what we convince ourselves is realistic.
But I believe in possibilities, and sometimes we have to redefine what is realistic." – Heather Moyse

Thursday
How I want to feel today:

☼

_____
_____
_____
_____
_____
_____

☀

_____
_____
_____
_____
_____

☾

_____
_____
_____

Friday
How I want to feel today:

☼

_____
_____
_____
_____
_____
_____

☀

_____
_____
_____
_____
_____

☾

_____
_____
_____

Saturday
How I want to feel today:

_____
_____
_____
_____
_____
_____
_____

Sunday
How I want to feel today:

_____
_____
_____
_____
_____
_____

Weekly Highlights & Successes

GRATITUDE LIST

_____
_____
_____
_____
_____
_____
_____

HABIT TRACKER

1 • _____
2 • _____
3 • _____
4 • _____
5 • _____
6 • _____
7 • _____

M	T	W	T	F	S	S
○	○	○	○	○	○	○
○	○	○	○	○	○	○
○	○	○	○	○	○	○
○	○	○	○	○	○	○
○	○	○	○	○	○	○
○	○	○	○	○	○	○
○	○	○	○	○	○	○

MONTH:

WEEK:

Monday
How I want to feel today:

Tuesday
How I want to feel today:

Wednesday
How I want to feel today:

GOALS

TASKS

NOTES

"Justice is something that should be accessible to everyone, not just the privileged." Cindy Blackstock

Thursday
How I want to feel today:

☼

_____
_____
_____
_____
_____

◐

_____
_____
_____
_____
_____

☾

_____
_____
_____
_____

Friday
How I want to feel today:

☼

_____
_____
_____
_____
_____

◐

_____
_____
_____
_____
_____

☾

_____
_____
_____
_____

Saturday
How I want to feel today:

_____
_____
_____
_____

Sunday
How I want to feel today:

_____
_____
_____
_____
_____

Weekly Highlights & Successes

GRATITUDE LIST

_____
_____
_____
_____
_____
_____

HABIT TRACKER

1 · _____
2 · _____
3 · _____
4 · _____
5 · _____
6 · _____
7 · _____

M	T	W	T	F	S	S
○	○	○	○	○	○	○
○	○	○	○	○	○	○
○	○	○	○	○	○	○
○	○	○	○	○	○	○
○	○	○	○	○	○	○
○	○	○	○	○	○	○
○	○	○	○	○	○	○

MONTH:

WEEK:

Monday
How I want to feel today:

Tuesday
How I want to feel today:

Wednesday
How I want to feel today:

GOALS

TASKS

NOTES

"It's rather simplistic but that's what it is: That there is room for redemption and hope, however grim things are; that the human spirit does have that ability to do something that is selfless, even under the most horrendous circumstances" - Deepa Mehta, filmmaker

Thursday
How I want to feel today:

☼

_____
_____
_____
_____
_____
_____

☀

_____
_____
_____
_____
_____

☾

_____
_____
_____
_____

Friday
How I want to feel today:

☼

_____
_____
_____
_____
_____
_____

☀

_____
_____
_____
_____
_____

☾

_____
_____
_____
_____

Saturday
How I want to feel today:

_____
_____
_____
_____

Sunday
How I want to feel today:

_____
_____
_____
_____
_____
_____

Weekly Highlights & Successes

GRATITUDE LIST

_____
_____
_____
_____
_____
_____
_____

HABIT TRACKER

1 • _____
2 • _____
3 • _____
4 • _____
5 • _____
6 • _____
7 • _____

M	T	W	T	F	S	S
○	○	○	○	○	○	○
○	○	○	○	○	○	○
○	○	○	○	○	○	○
○	○	○	○	○	○	○
○	○	○	○	○	○	○
○	○	○	○	○	○	○
○	○	○	○	○	○	○

MONTH:

WEEK:

Monday
How I want to feel today:

Tuesday
How I want to feel today:

Wednesday
How I want to feel today:

GOALS

- _____
- _____
- _____
- _____

TASKS

- _____
- _____
- _____
- _____
- _____
- _____
- _____
- _____
- _____
- _____
- _____
- _____

NOTES

"I had to learn to love myself by setting healthy boundaries and working through my trauma."
Elaine Alec -Author of "Calling My Spirit Back"

Thursday
How I want to feel today:

☼

_____
_____
_____
_____
_____

◐

_____
_____
_____
_____

☾

_____
_____
_____
_____

Friday
How I want to feel today:

☼

_____
_____
_____
_____
_____

◐

_____
_____
_____
_____

☾

_____
_____
_____
_____

Saturday
How I want to feel today:

_____
_____
_____
_____
_____

Sunday
How I want to feel today:

_____
_____
_____
_____
_____
_____

Weekly Highlights & Successes

GRATITUDE LIST

_____
_____
_____
_____
_____
_____
_____

HABIT TRACKER

1 • _____
2 • _____
3 • _____
4 • _____
5 • _____
6 • _____
7 • _____

M	T	W	T	F	S	S
○	○	○	○	○	○	○
○	○	○	○	○	○	○
○	○	○	○	○	○	○
○	○	○	○	○	○	○
○	○	○	○	○	○	○
○	○	○	○	○	○	○
○	○	○	○	○	○	○

Living
FULL CIRCLE

"Nothing I accept about myself can be used against me to diminish me."
- Audre Lorde

Accepting that life is not fair was one of my biggest breakthrough moments in life. Work towards viewing your troubles as blessings. There are many things in life that you cannot change. When you work towards accepting things that you cannot change, you place your power with yourself and the things you can control. It is through acceptance that you can move beyond the struggle.

In your healing journey, work to forgive those who have wronged you. Not for them, for you. It doesn't mean you have to allow them to be part of your life, but it does free your heart to no longer focus on the hurt. Your healing journey belongs to you; set your boundaries. Be kind to others and be especially kind to you.

The medicine wheel framework can help identify areas of your life that need attention. Reflecting on this through the process helps bring awareness to what is needed in your life.

 *Takeaways*

What were some of your most difficult experiences? What did you learn from them?

What are some things that you are struggling with now?

What are some options of moving beyond the struggle?

Quick tip: The process of writing a letter to those you haven't forgiven is a powerful experience that can help you with the healing process. The letter doesn't have to be sent; the process is meant for you.

Focus for the upcoming month

Current opportunities to explore

Actions that will serve my legacy

Important events

NOTES

MONTH:

WEEK:

Monday
How I want to feel today:

Tuesday
How I want to feel today:

Wednesday
How I want to feel today:

GOALS

○ _____
○ _____
○ _____
○ _____

TASKS

○ _____
○ _____
○ _____
○ _____
○ _____
○ _____
○ _____
○ _____
○ _____
○ _____
○ _____

☀

_____
_____
_____
_____
_____

🌤

_____
_____
_____

🌙

_____
_____
_____

☀

_____
_____
_____
_____
_____

🌤

_____
_____
_____

🌙

_____
_____
_____

☀

_____
_____
_____
_____
_____

🌤

_____
_____
_____

🌙

_____
_____
_____

NOTES

"It's time to remember it's time to summon our voices from the belly of the earth time to feel, cry, rage, heal, and truly live life instead. It is time to tell ourselves and our daughters the things that should have been said." - Helen Knott, Author

Thursday
How I want to feel today:

☼

_____
_____
_____
_____

☀

_____
_____
_____
_____

☾

_____
_____
_____

Friday
How I want to feel today:

☼

_____
_____
_____
_____

☀

_____
_____
_____
_____

☾

_____
_____
_____

Saturday
How I want to feel today:

_____
_____
_____
_____

Sunday
How I want to feel today:

_____
_____
_____
_____

Weekly Highlights & Successes

GRATITUDE LIST

_____
_____
_____
_____
_____
_____

HABIT TRACKER

1 • _____
2 • _____
3 • _____
4 • _____
5 • _____
6 • _____
7 • _____

M	T	W	T	F	S	S
○	○	○	○	○	○	○
○	○	○	○	○	○	○
○	○	○	○	○	○	○
○	○	○	○	○	○	○
○	○	○	○	○	○	○
○	○	○	○	○	○	○
○	○	○	○	○	○	○

MONTH: **WEEK:**

Monday
How I want to feel today:

Tuesday
How I want to feel today:

Wednesday
How I want to feel today:

GOALS

TASKS

NOTES

"I never learned how to be a woman in this world because I didn't know what it meant to be one. What I learned were things I was supposed to do and how to carry myself, but no one taught me to do that and trudge through my trauma at the same time." Elaine Alec, Author of "Calling My Spirit Back"

Thursday	**Friday**	**Saturday**	**Weekly Highlights & Successes**
How I want to feel today:	How I want to feel today:	How I want to feel today:	

☼

☼

_____
_____
_____
_____
_____
_____

☼

☼

_____
_____
_____
_____
_____
_____

☾

☾

_____
_____
_____
_____

Saturday:
_____
_____
_____
_____
_____
_____
_____
_____
_____
_____
_____

Sunday

How I want to feel today:

_____
_____
_____
_____
_____
_____
_____
_____

GRATITUDE LIST

_____
_____
_____
_____
_____
_____
_____

HABIT TRACKER

1 • _____
2 • _____
3 • _____
4 • _____
5 • _____
6 • _____
7 • _____

M	T	W	T	F	S	S
○	○	○	○	○	○	○
○	○	○	○	○	○	○
○	○	○	○	○	○	○
○	○	○	○	○	○	○
○	○	○	○	○	○	○
○	○	○	○	○	○	○
○	○	○	○	○	○	○

MONTH:

WEEK:

Monday
How I want to feel today:

Tuesday
How I want to feel today:

Wednesday
How I want to feel today:

GOALS

TASKS

NOTES

"If we can raise a generation of First Nations kids who never have to recover from their childhoods, and a generation of non-Indigenous children who never have to say they're sorry, then I think we have made a major step in co-creating a society that our ancestors always dreamed of, and that our great-great-great grandchildren would be proud of." - Cindy Blackstock

Thursday	Friday	Saturday	Weekly Highlights & Successes
How I want to feel today:	How I want to feel today:	How I want to feel today:	

☀ ☀

_____

_____
_____
_____
_____
_____

☀ ☀

_____
_____
_____
_____

Sunday

How I want to feel today:

🌙 🌙

_____
_____
_____
_____

GRATITUDE LIST

_____
_____
_____
_____
_____
_____
_____

HABIT TRACKER

1 • _____
2 • _____
3 • _____
4 • _____
5 • _____
6 • _____
7 • _____

M	T	W	T	F	S	S
○	○	○	○	○	○	○
○	○	○	○	○	○	○
○	○	○	○	○	○	○
○	○	○	○	○	○	○
○	○	○	○	○	○	○
○	○	○	○	○	○	○
○	○	○	○	○	○	○

MONTH:

WEEK:

Monday
How I want to feel today:

Tuesday
How I want to feel today:

Wednesday
How I want to feel today:

GOALS

- _____
- _____
- _____
- _____

TASKS

- _____
- _____
- _____
- _____
- _____
- _____
- _____
- _____
- _____
- _____
- _____
- _____

☼

☼

☼

☀

☀

☀

☾

☾

☾

NOTES

"Reconciliation means not having to say sorry a second time." - Cindy Blackstock

Thursday
How I want to feel today:

☼

_____
_____
_____
_____
_____

☀

_____
_____
_____
_____
_____

☾

_____
_____
_____
_____

Friday
How I want to feel today:

☼

_____
_____
_____
_____
_____

☀

_____
_____
_____
_____
_____

☾

_____
_____
_____
_____

Saturday
How I want to feel today:

_____
_____
_____

Sunday
How I want to feel today:

_____
_____
_____
_____
_____

Weekly Highlights & Successes

GRATITUDE LIST

_____
_____
_____
_____
_____
_____
_____

HABIT TRACKER

1 · _____
2 · _____
3 · _____
4 · _____
5 · _____
6 · _____
7 · _____

M	T	W	T	F	S	S
○	○	○	○	○	○	○
○	○	○	○	○	○	○
○	○	○	○	○	○	○
○	○	○	○	○	○	○
○	○	○	○	○	○	○
○	○	○	○	○	○	○
○	○	○	○	○	○	○

Your Authentic Self.

We have two ears and one mouth so that we can listen twice as much as we speak."
– Epictetus

Learn to sit comfortably in silence. In those moments you learn the most. Remember that you need to slow down to go fast! Rest is necessary. It doesn't serve you to stay full throttle all the time. When you slow down you are able to focus on revisiting and reflect on your purpose, needs, feelings and plans. This is essential work to provide you with direction in life. Save your energy for when it matters most.

Self-care is in your control. Care but don't carry!

 *Takeaways*

What does self-care look like for you?

What does rest look like for you?

How will you work to care, but not carry?

Quick tip: Focus on creating new habits (as opposed to fixing old ones), and creating lists of renewal tasks such as walking, disconnecting, being in nature, looking for balance, practicing mindfulness, journaling, decluttering, minimizing or simplifying, debriefing, resting, meditating, cleaning, and performing one task at a time.

Focus for the upcoming month

Current opportunities to explore

Actions that will serve my legacy

Important events

NOTES

MONTH:

WEEK:

Monday	**Tuesday**	**Wednesday**
How I want to feel today:	How I want to feel today:	How I want to feel today:

GOALS

TASKS

☼

☼

☼

☀

☀

☀

☾

☾

☾

NOTES

"Optimism means better than reality; pessimism means worse than reality. I'm a realist." - Margaret Atwood, Author

Thursday	Friday	Saturday	Weekly Highlights & Successes
How I want to feel today:	How I want to feel today:	How I want to feel today:	

☼

☼

_____
_____
_____
_____
_____

_____
_____
_____
_____
_____

_____
_____
_____

☀

☀

_____
_____
_____
_____
_____

_____
_____
_____
_____
_____

Sunday

How I want to feel today:

☾

☾

_____
_____
_____
_____

_____
_____
_____
_____

_____
_____
_____
_____
_____
_____

GRATITUDE LIST

_____
_____
_____
_____
_____
_____
_____

HABIT TRACKER

1 • _____
2 • _____
3 • _____
4 • _____
5 • _____
6 • _____
7 • _____

M	T	W	T	F	S	S
○	○	○	○	○	○	○
○	○	○	○	○	○	○
○	○	○	○	○	○	○
○	○	○	○	○	○	○
○	○	○	○	○	○	○
○	○	○	○	○	○	○
○	○	○	○	○	○	○

MONTH:

WEEK:

Monday
How I want to feel today:

Tuesday
How I want to feel today:

Wednesday
How I want to feel today:

GOALS

- _____
- _____
- _____
- _____

TASKS

- _____
- _____
- _____
- _____
- _____
- _____
- _____
- _____
- _____
- _____
- _____

☼

☼

☼

☽

☽

☽

NOTES

"The purpose of a woman's life is just the same as the purpose of a man's life: that she may make the best possible contribution to the generation in which she is living." - Louise McKinney

Thursday
How I want to feel today:

☼

_____
_____
_____
_____
_____

☼

_____
_____
_____
_____
_____

☾

_____
_____
_____
_____

Friday
How I want to feel today:

☼

_____
_____
_____
_____
_____

☼

_____
_____
_____
_____
_____

☾

_____
_____
_____
_____

Saturday
How I want to feel today:

_____
_____
_____
_____
_____

Sunday
How I want to feel today:

_____
_____
_____
_____
_____

Weekly Highlights & Successes

GRATITUDE LIST

_____
_____
_____
_____
_____
_____
_____

HABIT TRACKER

1 • _____
2 • _____
3 • _____
4 • _____
5 • _____
6 • _____
7 • _____

M	T	W	T	F	S	S
○	○	○	○	○	○	○
○	○	○	○	○	○	○
○	○	○	○	○	○	○
○	○	○	○	○	○	○
○	○	○	○	○	○	○
○	○	○	○	○	○	○
○	○	○	○	○	○	○

MONTH:

WEEK:

GOALS

_____
_____
_____
_____

TASKS

_____
_____
_____
_____
_____
_____
_____
_____
_____
_____
_____
_____

Monday

How I want to feel today:

☼

_____
_____
_____
_____
_____

🌓

_____
_____
_____
_____
_____

🌙

_____
_____
_____

Tuesday

How I want to feel today:

☼

_____
_____
_____
_____
_____

🌓

_____
_____
_____
_____
_____

🌙

_____
_____
_____

Wednesday

How I want to feel today:

☼

_____
_____
_____
_____
_____

🌓

_____
_____
_____
_____
_____

🌙

_____
_____
_____

NOTES

"Building of community, working together, and having faith is what creates change." - Cindy Blackstock

Thursday	Friday	Saturday	Weekly Highlights & Successes
How I want to feel today:	How I want to feel today:	How I want to feel today:	

☀

☀

_____
_____
_____
_____
_____
_____

☀

☀

_____
_____
_____
_____
_____
_____

🌙

🌙

_____
_____
_____
_____

Saturday:
_____
_____
_____
_____
_____
_____

Sunday

How I want to feel today:

_____
_____
_____
_____
_____
_____

GRATITUDE LIST

_____
_____
_____
_____
_____
_____
_____

HABIT TRACKER

1 • _____
2 • _____
3 • _____
4 • _____
5 • _____
6 • _____
7 • _____

M	T	W	T	F	S	S
○	○	○	○	○	○	○
○	○	○	○	○	○	○
○	○	○	○	○	○	○
○	○	○	○	○	○	○
○	○	○	○	○	○	○
○	○	○	○	○	○	○
○	○	○	○	○	○	○

MONTH:

WEEK:

Monday
How I want to feel today:

Tuesday
How I want to feel today:

Wednesday
How I want to feel today:

GOALS

TASKS

☀

☀

☀

🌤

🌤

🌤

☾

☾

☾

NOTES

"We still think of a powerful man as a born leader and a powerful woman as anomaly." Margaret Atwood

Thursday
How I want to feel today:

☼

_____
_____
_____
_____
_____
_____

☀

_____
_____
_____
_____
_____
_____

☾

_____
_____
_____
_____

Friday
How I want to feel today:

☼

_____
_____
_____
_____
_____
_____

☀

_____
_____
_____
_____
_____
_____

☾

_____
_____
_____
_____

Saturday
How I want to feel today:

_____
_____
_____
_____
_____
_____

Sunday
How I want to feel today:

_____
_____
_____
_____
_____
_____

Weekly Highlights & Successes

GRATITUDE LIST

_____
_____
_____
_____
_____
_____

HABIT TRACKER

1 • _____
2 • _____
3 • _____
4 • _____
5 • _____
6 • _____
7 • _____

M	T	W	T	F	S	S
○	○	○	○	○	○	○
○	○	○	○	○	○	○
○	○	○	○	○	○	○
○	○	○	○	○	○	○
○	○	○	○	○	○	○
○	○	○	○	○	○	○
○	○	○	○	○	○	○

Living
FULL CIRCLE

Resiliency, Stress and You!

"The strongest principle of growth lies in human choice."
George Eliot | Daniel Deronda

You deserve joy. You deserve space. You deserve healthy boundaries.
You deserve success. You deserve to live free from lateral violence.
You are free to disconnect from anything that isn't serving your wellbeing.

Core traits of resiliency include belonging, perspective, acceptance, hope and humour.
Incorporating joy and laughter are so important. Did you know that moments of joy
can actually block the negative? Choose happiness and joy, for you.

By identifying what you may be lacking in your life, you are incorporating balance and
intention. If your circle isn't full, you will feel it. Throughout this journey of becoming
more productive and achieving greater balance, be gentle with yourself.

Takeaways

What do you need to make your space safe?

What brings you joy?

How can you increase your happiness?

Quick tip: Keep going. Take one step at a time - forward is forward, no matter the pace.

Focus for the upcoming month

Current opportunities to explore

Actions that will serve my legacy

Important events

NOTES

MONTH:

WEEK:

Monday
How I want to feel today:

Tuesday
How I want to feel today:

Wednesday
How I want to feel today:

GOALS

TASKS

NOTES

"Our kids are our future. They deserve every possible opportunity to start their day with enthusiasm, encouragement and food in their stomachs. Protecting human rights of every man, woman and child is fundamental. Kids cannot protect themselves. It's up to us to ensure they have what they need to be all they can possibly be." – Arlene Dickinson, businesswoman and television personality

Thursday	Friday	Saturday	Weekly Highlights & Successes
How I want to feel today:	How I want to feel today:	How I want to feel today:	

☼   ☼

_____ _____ _____
_____ _____ _____
_____ _____ _____
_____ _____ _____
_____ _____ _____

🔆   🔆

Sunday

How I want to feel today:

_____ _____
_____ _____
_____ _____
_____ _____
_____ _____

🌙   🌙

_____ _____ _____
_____ _____ _____
_____ _____ _____
_____ _____ _____

GRATITUDE LIST

_____
_____
_____
_____
_____
_____
_____

HABIT TRACKER

1 • _____
2 • _____
3 • _____
4 • _____
5 • _____
6 • _____
7 • _____

M	T	W	T	F	S	S
○	○	○	○	○	○	○
○	○	○	○	○	○	○
○	○	○	○	○	○	○
○	○	○	○	○	○	○
○	○	○	○	○	○	○
○	○	○	○	○	○	○
○	○	○	○	○	○	○

MONTH:

WEEK:

Monday
How I want to feel today:

Tuesday
How I want to feel today:

Wednesday
How I want to feel today:

GOALS

- _____
- _____
- _____
- _____

TASKS

- _____
- _____
- _____
- _____
- _____
- _____
- _____
- _____
- _____
- _____
- _____
- _____
- _____

NOTES

"You are the first teacher to your children. Lead by example." – Elder Carolyn Sark

Thursday	**Friday**	**Saturday**	**Weekly Highlights & Successes**

Thursday
How I want to feel today:

☼
_____
_____
_____
_____
_____

☼
_____
_____
_____
_____
_____

☾
_____
_____
_____

Friday
How I want to feel today:

☼
_____
_____
_____
_____
_____

☼
_____
_____
_____
_____
_____

☾
_____
_____
_____

Saturday
How I want to feel today:

_____
_____
_____
_____

Sunday
How I want to feel today:

_____
_____
_____
_____
_____

Weekly Highlights & Successes

GRATITUDE LIST

_____
_____
_____
_____
_____
_____
_____

HABIT TRACKER

1 • _____
2 • _____
3 • _____
4 • _____
5 • _____
6 • _____
7 • _____

M	T	W	T	F	S	S
○	○	○	○	○	○	○
○	○	○	○	○	○	○
○	○	○	○	○	○	○
○	○	○	○	○	○	○
○	○	○	○	○	○	○
○	○	○	○	○	○	○
○	○	○	○	○	○	○

MONTH:

WEEK:

Monday
How I want to feel today:

Tuesday
How I want to feel today:

Wednesday
How I want to feel today:

GOALS

TASKS

☀

☀

☀

☽

☽

☽

NOTES

"I am from anywhere and everywhere. Eskasoni is the place I choose to live, but I am not from there. We say we are from Mi'kma'ki."
– Dr. Murdena Marshall

Thursday
How I want to feel today:

☀

_____
_____
_____
_____
_____

🌓

_____
_____
_____
_____
_____

🌙

_____
_____
_____
_____

Friday
How I want to feel today:

☀

_____
_____
_____
_____
_____

🌓

_____
_____
_____
_____
_____

🌙

_____
_____
_____
_____

Saturday
How I want to feel today:

_____
_____
_____
_____
_____
_____

Sunday
How I want to feel today:

_____
_____
_____
_____
_____

Weekly Highlights & Successes

GRATITUDE LIST

_____
_____
_____
_____
_____
_____
_____

HABIT TRACKER

1 • _____
2 • _____
3 • _____
4 • _____
5 • _____
6 • _____
7 • _____

M	T	W	T	F	S	S
○	○	○	○	○	○	○
○	○	○	○	○	○	○
○	○	○	○	○	○	○
○	○	○	○	○	○	○
○	○	○	○	○	○	○
○	○	○	○	○	○	○
○	○	○	○	○	○	○

MONTH:　　　　　　　　　**WEEK:**

| **Monday** | **Tuesday** | **Wednesday** |
| How I want to feel today: | How I want to feel today: | How I want to feel today: |

GOALS

_____
_____
_____
_____

TASKS

_____
_____
_____
_____
_____
_____
_____
_____
_____
_____
_____
_____

☼

☀

☾

NOTES

"Our people are awakening, it brings me joy to see community empowerment and Indigenous women rising and living and creating beyond fabricated limitations" - Carol Anne Hilton CEO and Founder of the Indigenomics Institute and author of 'Indigenomics - Taking A Seat At The Economic Table'

Thursday
How I want to feel today:

☼

_____
_____
_____
_____
_____
_____

◐

_____
_____
_____
_____
_____

☾

_____
_____
_____
_____

Friday
How I want to feel today:

☼

_____
_____
_____
_____
_____
_____

◐

_____
_____
_____
_____
_____

☾

_____
_____
_____
_____

Saturday
How I want to feel today:

_____
_____
_____
_____
_____

Sunday
How I want to feel today:

_____
_____
_____
_____
_____

Weekly Highlights & Successes

GRATITUDE LIST

_____
_____
_____
_____
_____
_____
_____

HABIT TRACKER

1 · _____
2 · _____
3 · _____
4 · _____
5 · _____
6 · _____
7 · _____

M	T	W	T	F	S	S
○	○	○	○	○	○	○
○	○	○	○	○	○	○
○	○	○	○	○	○	○
○	○	○	○	○	○	○
○	○	○	○	○	○	○
○	○	○	○	○	○	○
○	○	○	○	○	○	○

Brave Choices.

"The only constant in life is change." - Heraclitus

The more you accept change and work with it, the easier change is. Things are constantly changing; they either are moving forwards or backwards. Your choices impact your future. Believe you have the strength to deal with whatever comes your way.

Don't be scared to ask for what you want. Most people don't read minds! The worst response you could receive is no, and then at least you know where you stand.

The interconnectedness of doing, thinking, feeling and experiencing in each of the medicine wheel quadrants impacts our choices, and our choices impact our wellbeing.

 *Takeaways*

What is it that you fear? Take yourself to the worst-case scenario and work yourself back.

What if the worst-case scenario happened?

What are options to work through worst-case scenerios?

Quick tip: Before you act, decide exactly what it is you want and be ready to communicate it clearly.

Focus for the upcoming month

Current opportunities to explore

Actions that will serve my legacy

Important events

NOTES

MONTH:　　　　　　　　　　　**WEEK:**

Monday
How I want to feel today:

Tuesday
How I want to feel today:

Wednesday
How I want to feel today:

GOALS

- _____
- _____
- _____
- _____

TASKS

- _____
- _____
- _____
- _____
- _____
- _____
- _____
- _____
- _____
- _____
- _____
- _____

NOTES

"Empower women and you will see a decrease in poverty, disease and violence." Michaëlle Jean

Thursday
How I want to feel today:

☼

_____
_____
_____
_____

🔅

_____
_____
_____
_____

☾

_____
_____
_____

Friday
How I want to feel today:

☼

_____
_____
_____
_____

🔅

_____
_____
_____
_____

☾

_____
_____
_____

Saturday
How I want to feel today:

_____
_____
_____
_____
_____

Sunday
How I want to feel today:

_____
_____
_____
_____

Weekly Highlights & Successes

GRATITUDE LIST

_____
_____
_____
_____
_____
_____
_____

HABIT TRACKER

1 • _____
2 • _____
3 • _____
4 • _____
5 • _____
6 • _____
7 • _____

M	T	W	T	F	S	S
○	○	○	○	○	○	○
○	○	○	○	○	○	○
○	○	○	○	○	○	○
○	○	○	○	○	○	○
○	○	○	○	○	○	○
○	○	○	○	○	○	○
○	○	○	○	○	○	○

MONTH:

WEEK:

Monday
How I want to feel today:

Tuesday
How I want to feel today:

Wednesday
How I want to feel today:

GOALS

TASKS

☼

☼

☼

☼

☼

☼

☾

☾

☾

NOTES

"My political perspective as a socialist feminist provides a framework for understanding what I see. But feminism taught me to listen to other women." - Judy Rebick, feminist

Thursday
How I want to feel today:

☼

_____
_____
_____
_____
_____

☀

_____
_____
_____
_____
_____

☾

_____
_____
_____
_____
_____

Friday
How I want to feel today:

☼

_____
_____
_____
_____
_____

☀

_____
_____
_____
_____
_____

☾

_____
_____
_____
_____
_____

Saturday
How I want to feel today:

_____
_____
_____
_____
_____

Sunday
How I want to feel today:

_____
_____
_____
_____
_____

Weekly Highlights & Successes

GRATITUDE LIST

_____
_____
_____
_____
_____
_____
_____

HABIT TRACKER

1 · _____
2 · _____
3 · _____
4 · _____
5 · _____
6 · _____
7 · _____

M	T	W	T	F	S	S
○	○	○	○	○	○	○
○	○	○	○	○	○	○
○	○	○	○	○	○	○
○	○	○	○	○	○	○
○	○	○	○	○	○	○
○	○	○	○	○	○	○
○	○	○	○	○	○	○

MONTH:　　　　　　　　　　**WEEK:**

Monday
How I want to feel today:

Tuesday
How I want to feel today:

Wednesday
How I want to feel today:

GOALS

TASKS

NOTES

"Women had first to convince the world that they had souls and then that they had minds and then it came on to this matter of political entity and the end is not yet...." - Nellie McClung, activist and author

Thursday
How I want to feel today:

☀

_____
_____
_____
_____
_____

☼

_____
_____
_____
_____

☾

_____
_____
_____

Friday
How I want to feel today:

☀

_____
_____
_____
_____
_____

☼

_____
_____
_____
_____

☾

_____
_____
_____

Saturday
How I want to feel today:

_____
_____
_____
_____
_____
_____

Sunday
How I want to feel today:

_____
_____
_____
_____
_____

Weekly Highlights & Successes

GRATITUDE LIST

_____
_____
_____
_____
_____
_____

HABIT TRACKER

1 • _____
2 • _____
3 • _____
4 • _____
5 • _____
6 • _____
7 • _____

M	T	W	T	F	S	S
○	○	○	○	○	○	○
○	○	○	○	○	○	○
○	○	○	○	○	○	○
○	○	○	○	○	○	○
○	○	○	○	○	○	○
○	○	○	○	○	○	○
○	○	○	○	○	○	○

MONTH:

WEEK:

Monday
How I want to feel today:

Tuesday
How I want to feel today:

Wednesday
How I want to feel today:

GOALS

TASKS

NOTES

"I really believe in the goodness of Canadians. The idea that everyone should be given an equal opportunity to succeed in this country and particularly for children." - Cindy Blackstock

Thursday
How I want to feel today:

☼

_____
_____
_____
_____
_____

☀

_____
_____
_____
_____

☾

_____
_____
_____
_____

Friday
How I want to feel today:

☼

_____
_____
_____
_____
_____

☀

_____
_____
_____
_____

☾

_____
_____
_____
_____

Saturday
How I want to feel today:

_____
_____
_____

Sunday
How I want to feel today:

_____
_____
_____
_____
_____

Weekly Highlights & Successes

GRATITUDE LIST

_____
_____
_____
_____
_____
_____
_____

HABIT TRACKER

1 · _____
2 · _____
3 · _____
4 · _____
5 · _____
6 · _____
7 · _____

M	T	W	T	F	S	S
○	○	○	○	○	○	○
○	○	○	○	○	○	○
○	○	○	○	○	○	○
○	○	○	○	○	○	○
○	○	○	○	○	○	○
○	○	○	○	○	○	○
○	○	○	○	○	○	○

Control Over Yourself.

"The willingness to accept responsibility for one's own life is the source from which self-respect springs." - Joan Didion

It's all about you; you are only responsible for yourself and the energy you bring to the world. You don't have control over how other people act or react. The medicine wheel reflection helps you with inward reflection and control that you have over yourself. How you behave, how you feel, what you are lacking, and what you need.

 *Takeaways*

What would it look like to live authentically?

Do your actions align with your words?

What are ways you want to improve yourself?

Quick tip: Don't waste your energy on others or things that don't serve you.

Focus for the upcoming month

Current opportunities to explore

Actions that will serve my legacy

Important events

NOTES

MONTH: _____ WEEK: _____

Monday
How I want to feel today:

Tuesday
How I want to feel today:

Wednesday
How I want to feel today:

GOALS

- _____
- _____
- _____
- _____

TASKS

- _____
- _____
- _____
- _____
- _____
- _____
- _____
- _____
- _____
- _____
- _____

☼

_____
_____
_____
_____
_____

☼

_____
_____
_____
_____
_____

☾

_____
_____
_____

☼

_____
_____
_____
_____
_____

☼

_____
_____
_____
_____
_____

☾

_____
_____
_____

☼

_____
_____
_____
_____
_____

☼

_____
_____
_____
_____
_____

☾

_____
_____
_____

NOTES

"War is what happens when language fails." - Margaret Atwood, Author

Thursday
How I want to feel today:

☼

_____
_____
_____
_____
_____

☼

_____
_____
_____
_____

☾

_____
_____
_____

Friday
How I want to feel today:

☼

_____
_____
_____
_____
_____

☼

_____
_____
_____
_____

☾

_____
_____
_____

Saturday
How I want to feel today:

_____
_____
_____
_____

Sunday
How I want to feel today:

_____
_____
_____
_____
_____

Weekly Highlights & Successes

GRATITUDE LIST

_____
_____
_____
_____
_____
_____
_____

HABIT TRACKER

1 • _____
2 • _____
3 • _____
4 • _____
5 • _____
6 • _____
7 • _____

M	T	W	T	F	S	S
○	○	○	○	○	○	○
○	○	○	○	○	○	○
○	○	○	○	○	○	○
○	○	○	○	○	○	○
○	○	○	○	○	○	○
○	○	○	○	○	○	○
○	○	○	○	○	○	○

MONTH:

WEEK:

Monday
How I want to feel today:

Tuesday
How I want to feel today:

Wednesday
How I want to feel today:

GOALS

TASKS

☀

☀

☀

🌓

🌓

🌓

🌙

🌙

🌙

NOTES

"If I waited for perfection, I would never write a word." - Margaret Atwood, Author

Thursday	**Friday**	**Saturday**	**Weekly Highlights & Successes**
How I want to feel today:	How I want to feel today:	How I want to feel today:	

☼

☼

_____
_____
_____
_____
_____

☼

☼

Sunday

How I want to feel today:

_____
_____
_____
_____
_____

☾

☾

GRATITUDE LIST

_____
_____
_____
_____
_____
_____
_____

HABIT TRACKER

1 • _____
2 • _____
3 • _____
4 • _____
5 • _____
6 • _____
7 • _____

M	T	W	T	F	S	S
○	○	○	○	○	○	○
○	○	○	○	○	○	○
○	○	○	○	○	○	○
○	○	○	○	○	○	○
○	○	○	○	○	○	○
○	○	○	○	○	○	○
○	○	○	○	○	○	○

Living
FULL CIRCLE

MONTH:

WEEK:

Monday	**Tuesday**	**Wednesday**
How I want to feel today:	How I want to feel today:	How I want to feel today:

GOALS

- _____
- _____
- _____
- _____

TASKS

- _____
- _____
- _____
- _____
- _____
- _____
- _____
- _____
- _____
- _____
- _____
- _____

NOTES

"What is believed in society is not always the equivalent of what is true; but as regards to a woman's reputation, it amounts to the same thing." - Margaret Atwood, Author

Thursday	**Friday**	**Saturday**	**Weekly Highlights & Successes**
How I want to feel today:	How I want to feel today:	How I want to feel today:	

☼

☼

_____

_____   _____   _____

_____   _____   _____

_____   _____   _____

_____   _____   _____

_____   _____   _____

_____   _____   _____

☼   ☼

Sunday

How I want to feel today:

_____   _____

_____   _____

_____   _____

_____   _____

_____   _____   _____

☾   ☾

_____

_____   _____   _____

_____   _____   _____

_____   _____   _____

_____   _____   _____

GRATITUDE LIST

HABIT TRACKER

_____   1 • _____

_____   2 • _____

_____   3 • _____

_____   4 • _____

_____   5 • _____

_____   6 • _____

_____   7 • _____

M	T	W	T	F	S	S
○	○	○	○	○	○	○
○	○	○	○	○	○	○
○	○	○	○	○	○	○
○	○	○	○	○	○	○
○	○	○	○	○	○	○
○	○	○	○	○	○	○
○	○	○	○	○	○	○

MONTH:

WEEK:

Monday
How I want to feel today:

Tuesday
How I want to feel today:

Wednesday
How I want to feel today:

GOALS

- _____
- _____
- _____
- _____

TASKS

- _____
- _____
- _____
- _____
- _____
- _____
- _____
- _____
- _____
- _____
- _____
- _____
- _____

☼

☼

☼

☀

☀

☀

☾

☾

☾

NOTES

"The whole idea of the feminist struggle being a peripheral kind of thing that you do in your spare time is something that has to be changed." - Rosemary Brown

Thursday	Friday	Saturday	Weekly Highlights & Successes
How I want to feel today:	How I want to feel today:	How I want to feel today:	

☼

☼

_____

_____

_____

_____

_____

_____

_____

_____

_____

_____

☀

☀

Sunday
How I want to feel today:

_____

_____

_____

_____

_____

_____

☾

☾

_____

_____

_____

_____

_____

_____

_____

_____

GRATITUDE LIST

_____

_____

_____

_____

_____

_____

_____

HABIT TRACKER

1 • _____
2 • _____
3 • _____
4 • _____
5 • _____
6 • _____
7 • _____

M	T	W	T	F	S	S
○	○	○	○	○	○	○
○	○	○	○	○	○	○
○	○	○	○	○	○	○
○	○	○	○	○	○	○
○	○	○	○	○	○	○
○	○	○	○	○	○	○
○	○	○	○	○	○	○

Reflection.

"Who you are tomorrow begins with what you do today" - Tim Fargo

Congratulations! You've almost completed a full year dedicated to Living Full Circle and I hope you are ready to reflect on your success, where you are in your life now, and what your plans are for the year ahead. It amazes me how much can be accomplished in a year, and if we do this every year, how far we can go.

The medicine wheel helps us on our journey of seeking balance for our spirit. It gives us an opportunity to reflect on our journey and how we want our journey to be. This builds our own self-awareness, which is key to understanding ourselves. You were able to identify what your needs were in each of the quadrants and reflect on what you want to do and how you want to be each week.

Remember, there is no such thing as perfection; you are a work in progress. Being aware of where you are in your life, and what you want in your life is huge. I hope that you continue to have more balance in your life and you continue on your path of growth and success.

 *Takeaways*

How have you improved balance in your life?

How will you celebrate your successes?

What does growth look like for you this year?

Quick tip: Nothing changes if nothing changes.

Focus for the upcoming month

Current opportunities to explore

Actions that will serve my legacy

Important events

NOTES

MONTH: **WEEK:**

Monday
How I want to feel today:

Tuesday
How I want to feel today:

Wednesday
How I want to feel today:

GOALS

- _____
- _____
- _____
- _____

TASKS

- _____
- _____
- _____
- _____
- _____
- _____
- _____
- _____
- _____
- _____
- _____

☼

☼

☼

◑

◑

◑

☾

☾

☾

NOTES

"If politics mean...the effort to secure through legislative action better conditions of life for the people, greater opportunities for our children and other people's children...then it most assuredly is a woman's job as much as it is a man's job."- Irene Parlbly

Thursday
How I want to feel today:

☼

_____
_____
_____
_____
_____
_____

☼

_____
_____
_____
_____
_____
_____

☾

_____
_____
_____
_____

Friday
How I want to feel today:

☼

_____
_____
_____
_____
_____
_____

☼

_____
_____
_____
_____
_____
_____

☾

_____
_____
_____
_____

Saturday
How I want to feel today:

_____
_____
_____
_____
_____
_____

Sunday
How I want to feel today:

_____
_____
_____
_____
_____

Weekly Highlights & Successes

GRATITUDE LIST

_____
_____
_____
_____
_____
_____
_____

HABIT TRACKER

1 · _____
2 · _____
3 · _____
4 · _____
5 · _____
6 · _____
7 · _____

M	T	W	T	F	S	S
○	○	○	○	○	○	○
○	○	○	○	○	○	○
○	○	○	○	○	○	○
○	○	○	○	○	○	○
○	○	○	○	○	○	○
○	○	○	○	○	○	○
○	○	○	○	○	○	○

MONTH:

WEEK:

Monday
How I want to feel today:

Tuesday
How I want to feel today:

Wednesday
How I want to feel today:

GOALS

TASKS

NOTES

"If I had the choice—which I do not—I would choose better political conditions and literary obscurity." - Margaret Atwood, Author

Thursday
How I want to feel today:

☼
_____
_____
_____
_____
_____

☀
_____
_____
_____
_____

☾
_____
_____
_____

Friday
How I want to feel today:

☼
_____
_____
_____
_____
_____

☀
_____
_____
_____
_____

☾
_____
_____
_____

Saturday
How I want to feel today:

_____
_____
_____
_____
_____
_____

Sunday
How I want to feel today:

_____
_____
_____
_____
_____
_____

Weekly Highlights & Successes

GRATITUDE LIST

_____
_____
_____
_____
_____
_____
_____

HABIT TRACKER

1 • _____
2 • _____
3 • _____
4 • _____
5 • _____
6 • _____
7 • _____

M	T	W	T	F	S	S
○	○	○	○	○	○	○
○	○	○	○	○	○	○
○	○	○	○	○	○	○
○	○	○	○	○	○	○
○	○	○	○	○	○	○
○	○	○	○	○	○	○
○	○	○	○	○	○	○

MONTH:

WEEK:

Monday
How I want to feel today:

Tuesday
How I want to feel today:

Wednesday
How I want to feel today:

GOALS

TASKS

NOTES

"Every one of us has to do what I did and that is to kick yourself over that line where life leads into darkness and realize that you have to be a hero for kids." - Cindy Blackstock

Thursday
How I want to feel today:

☼

_____
_____
_____
_____
_____
_____

☼

_____
_____
_____
_____
_____
_____

☾

_____
_____
_____
_____

Friday
How I want to feel today:

☼

_____
_____
_____
_____
_____
_____

☼

_____
_____
_____
_____
_____
_____

☾

_____
_____
_____
_____

Saturday
How I want to feel today:

_____
_____
_____
_____
_____

Sunday
How I want to feel today:

_____
_____
_____
_____
_____
_____

Weekly Highlights & Successes

GRATITUDE LIST

_____
_____
_____
_____
_____
_____

HABIT TRACKER

1 · _____
2 · _____
3 · _____
4 · _____
5 · _____
6 · _____
7 · _____

M	T	W	T	F	S	S
○	○	○	○	○	○	○
○	○	○	○	○	○	○
○	○	○	○	○	○	○
○	○	○	○	○	○	○
○	○	○	○	○	○	○
○	○	○	○	○	○	○
○	○	○	○	○	○	○

MONTH:

WEEK:

Monday
How I want to feel today:

Tuesday
How I want to feel today:

Wednesday
How I want to feel today:

GOALS

_____
_____
_____
_____

TASKS

_____
_____
_____
_____
_____
_____
_____
_____
_____
_____
_____
_____

☼

☼

☼

◐

◐

◐

☾

☾

☾

NOTES

"In the end, we all become stories." - Margaret Atwood, Author

Thursday	Friday	Saturday	Weekly Highlights & Successes

Thursday
How I want to feel today:

☼

_____
_____
_____
_____
_____

☼☽

_____
_____
_____
_____
_____

☾

_____
_____
_____

Friday
How I want to feel today:

☼

_____
_____
_____
_____
_____

☼☽

_____
_____
_____
_____
_____

☾

_____
_____
_____

Saturday
How I want to feel today:

_____
_____
_____
_____
_____

Sunday
How I want to feel today:

_____
_____
_____
_____
_____

Weekly Highlights & Successes

GRATITUDE LIST

_____
_____
_____
_____
_____
_____
_____

HABIT TRACKER

1 • _____
2 • _____
3 • _____
4 • _____
5 • _____
6 • _____
7 • _____

M	T	W	T	F	S	S
○	○	○	○	○	○	○
○	○	○	○	○	○	○
○	○	○	○	○	○	○
○	○	○	○	○	○	○
○	○	○	○	○	○	○
○	○	○	○	○	○	○
○	○	○	○	○	○	○

"Be the snowflake that flutters from the sky, full of beauty and hope. Be the one that makes a difference, be the one who becomes the change. Because once you know you must try and change the world, you will be just the same as I."

- Knowledge Keeper, Julie Pellisier-Lush

Dedication

To my family - My mother Carolyn for your love and commitment, my father Jim for your dedication to making life better for your community and family, my husband Cale, for being my partner in living our best life and for your unwavering love and support to me and our children, and the light of my world - Taite and Taya for showing me how far I could push myself and a love I didn't know existed.

To those powerhouse women who
have provided support and friendship throughout my journey.

To Indigenous women everywhere who
are doing their best in a world that is not designed for them.

To everyone committed to personal and professional
development and a growth mindset.

To changemakers and strong women
who hold space for those who need it most.

Msit No'kmaq/All My Relations
Wela'lioq/Thank You